# LISA FREEMAN

SCHOLASTIC BOOK SERVICES
New York Toronto London Auckland Sydney Tokyo

ISBN 0-590-30877-7

12 11 10 9 8 7 6 5 4 3 2 1    11            9/7 0 1 2 3 4/8

# CONTENTS

# Jimmy McNichol: Fever! California Style

Cruising around in cars! It's the favorite way to go for most young Americans — especially on the West Coast. After school and particularly during summer, guys and girls hop into their cars or vans and drive up and down the busiest and most popular streets in town, looking for friends and fun happenings.

That's where the idea for a TV show called *California Fever* came from. In Los Angeles, one of the areas with a lot of cruisers is Van Nuys Boulevard; another is the stretch along the beach at Malibu. And those are the places where the cast and crew of this new series went to do the filming for the weekly shows.

Jimmy McNichol stars as Vince Butler, a guy

with a dressed-up van. With his friend, Ross Whitman, played by Marc McClure, they meet friends, have fun, and often share some highly entertaining adventures.

If the name Jimmy McNichol sounds familiar to you, there's a good reason why. Jimmy's sister is the talented actress, Kristy McNichol, of TV's *Family*; and Jimmy used to host a TV show, *Hollywood Teen*. Last year he made an album with his sister. And Jimmy also won great reviews for his performance in the TV movie, *Champions: A Love Story*, about two young figure skaters trying to make the Olympics.

Jimmy's first commercial was at the age of six, and Kristy's was at age seven. Recently, another brother, Tommy, now 15, has stepped into acting — so far, mostly in commercials.

Kristy and Jimmy's first record album had a good reception, and they are planning another joint singing effort. "She's the choreographer for us," says Jimmy, talking about the song and dance routine they put together. "She's very good at making up precision dance steps."

"But he's more relaxed," Kristy puts in. "He knows how to move and make it look good."

"Kristy's a better singer, though," Jimmy adds — to get in the last word.

Although Jimmy is very busy at work these

days and doesn't have a lot of time to spend with his family, he is still very close to them.

A few months ago, he bought a house of his own — not far from where his mom, Carolyn McNichol, and Kristy live. Jimmy just recently turned 18, and his mother knows he is reliable and responsible, as well as independent. He shares his split-level home with his good friend and cousin, Jimbo — and he also keeps three Great Danes and a couple of horses. (The dogs live in, but not the horses!)

Horses have always been a big part of Jimmy's life. Besides being an excellent rider, Jimmy is also president of a fan club for a *single* horse! Jimmy felt this horse was so special, he deserved a following of his own. Dash for Cash is the name of the horse — and the name of the club. The horse is a two-time world champion quarter horse, with a major race, the Skoal Dash for Cash Futurity, named for him.

But Jimmy's interest isn't so much in the money or even the racing. What he wants to see is more teens interested in horses and riding. He plans to use his position as president of the fan club to raise money for charity.

"It makes sense to me," Jimmy says. "Why should fan clubs be just for movie stars and singers? Dash for Cash is a real champion, and his fans should get together." Jimmy plans to show support for his horse idol through horse clubs around the nation. He wants the Dash for Cash teenage brigade to get involved in raising money for specific charities.

Like Vince in *California Fever*, Jimmy, (whose middle name is Vincent), has a 1971 Chevy van he's been working on for the past several months. His van now sports a sun roof, portholes, tinted windows, curtains, panels, high-backed seats, and a stereo. Jimmy has done all the work himself. He uses the van mostly for going to the beach or to a drive-in movie; for business appointments, he has another car — a Porsche.

Besides his interest in horses and cars, Jimmy's an avid skateboard rider, scuba diver, and ice skater, and also enjoys skiing and photography. His interest in skateboarding goes beyond the average. He really takes it seriously and would like to organize public opinion in favor of skateboard representation at the Olympics. "It's more than a fad," Jimmy says. "It's a sport that can be controlled — and it's international. It's big in Europe, Australia, and South Africa."

Jimmy's really excited about his new series and says part of the fun is being able to film outdoors. Since *California Fever* is about a group of young guys who hang out at the beach,

Jimmy McNichol was really excited about overhauling his car so he could use it on *California Fever*. But just as he was putting on the finishing touches, the car rolled down a hill into a barn, and was totaled!

and Jimmy's character is a lifeguard, "We get to spend a lot of time on the beach."

Jimmy found a new best friend in co-star Marc McClure. Marc's a few years older, and shares many of the same interests. "Our TV characters aren't that different from how we are in real life," Jimmy says.

Both Jimmy and Marc loved the movie *Superman* — but for a special reason. Marc starred as Jimmy Olsen, cub photographer for the *Metropolis Daily Planet* newspaper.

By answering just one question right, Marc got the role of Olsen in the movie. Director Richard Donner asked him, "Do you have any idea who Jimmy Olsen is?"

"Golly, Mr. Kent, sure I do," was McClure's reply, and with that, he was signed for the part.

"I had exactly one day to get a passport, get vaccinated, and fly to London to begin rehearsals," Marc recalls. "I had never been out of the United States before. Come to think of it, I'd never been out of California, either."

Maybe being such a California guy was the one thing that got Marc the part in *California Fever*. He fits in perfectly with the fun-in-the-sun California lifestyle that's reflected in the new series.

Off screen, like Jimmy, he loves sports, especially golf and football. He's excited about his first television series because he and Jimmy have a great working relationship. Their excitement comes across even on the smallest TV screen, every time they come cruising into homes across the nation, bringing that "California Fever" with them.

# Robin Williams:
## *Mork and Mindy*
# Races On!

Nanu, Nanu! Robin Williams and Pam Dawber have moved out! But don't worry; it's just that all the action on the show has been moved from Mindy's dad's music store to a delicatessen, where Mindy works part-time to help put herself through college.

Of course you'll probably miss Grandma Cora Hudson, played by Elizabeth Kerr, and Fred McConnel, played by Conrad Janis. Although they've been written out of the show this season, they could be back as guest stars. They've been replaced by three new characters who keep things hopping at the deli: Mindy's cousin, Nelson, and Remo and Jean DeVinci. Remo and Jean are a brother and sister team who own the deli in Boulder, the town where Mork is learning all about life on Earth.

Like last season, *Mork and Mindy* will continue to be more than just a situation comedy. Each week, besides the silly adventures and jokes, there's a lesson to be learned. Struggling through life on Earth, Mork continues, with Mindy's help, to learn about faith, trust, love, understanding — and a few bad things, too, like greed, bigotry, and maybe even rising prices and pollution.

Life on the set of *Mork and Mindy* is always a lot of fun. Pam Dawber says the biggest problem working with Robin is trying to keep a straight face. "Most of the time I don't know what Robin's going to do," says Pam. "I end up laughing hysterically, and sometimes it's a miracle we get the scenes shot at all!"

Robin Williams today is a lot different than he was while growing up. As a youngster he was quiet and shy and didn't have any friends. Born in Chicago, Robin grew up in a wealthy family and was raised in the suburbs of Detroit in a 30-room mansion. Although he has two older half brothers, they were already grown up by the time Robin came along. So he was raised like an only child and he led a very solitary life, his imagination substituting for friends. "I used to spend hours in the basement," Robin recalls, "playing with my collection of two thousand toy soldiers. I had all these voices I would use, and sound effects, and I would entertain myself. I was fat, too, and wore a blazer and carried a briefcase to school. The other kids called me 'dwarf' and 'leprechaun' so I took up wrestling to get rid of my hostility and anger — and lost thirty pounds. That's when I started comedy stuff."

When his family moved to California, it helped Robin come out of his shell a little more. While attending Claremont Men's College (he was planning on going into the business world) he discovered an interest in the theater. He then went on to study Shakespeare at the College of Marin, and won a scholarship to The Juilliard School to study drama for three years.

"Living in New York helped mature me," Robin says. Then he headed for San Francisco to try to make it as a serious actor. But he discovered it was a hard field to break into, so he turned to comedy. In the summer of 1976, in Los Angeles, he performed at The Comedy Store — a club for new comedians. "My stomach was in my shoes, I was so scared, but after a while I felt comfortable. I knew I could make people laugh." Robin smiles.

From there Robin went on to star in the comedy series *Laugh-In*, and then did a guest appearance on *Happy Days*, playing a spaceman from the Planet Ork. The mail reaction to this episode was so great, ABC-TV ordered a whole series starring Mork — and that's when it all began happening!

On the *Mork and Mindy* set, it's easy to see how much Robin enjoys playing Mork. "I just love improvising and having a good time working. If you're having a good time, everybody enjoys themselves," Robin believes. But it's more than that. Robin is special, magnetic, and talented, and loves being with his co-stars and the crew. Everyone can sense it and it keeps the good feeling flowing during the long work week.

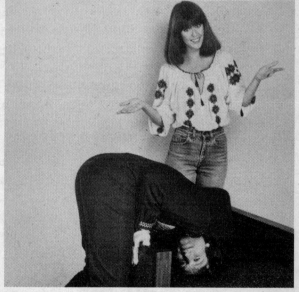

It's as easy as one, two, three to get ahead in Orkan social circles, but on Earth, Mork may have a little more trouble.

Robin's dressing room on the Paramount Studio lot has his name on the door in big letters. Inside there's a refrigerator filled with Perrier water and organic juices, which he drinks constantly. A non-smoking vegetarian who keeps his five-foot, eight-inch frame at 140 pounds with a daily three-mile jog, Robin's also into yoga, dance exercises, roller skating, swimming, and backgammon.

He lives with his wife, Valerie, in a new house in the mountains near Los Angeles, which they share with a parrot, two lizards, and an iguana. On weekends and when the show isn't being taped, the couple head to another house near the beach. That is, if Robin's not doing comedy routines at small clubs in the evenings.

Busy is a good word to describe Robin. He's up at dawn to drive into Hollywood. Taping the show takes the entire week. Robin's also working on a screenplay, and he's just released his first comedy album. He also got the lead in his first motion picture, *Popeye* — playing, of course, the spinach-loving hero.

For all his success, Robin has retained his friendly, zany, warm outlook on life. You might think his popularity would have given him a swelled head, but it hasn't, and his co-star, Pam Dawber, is the first to say so.

She likes to recall the first day of taping, when she and Robin had to hold coffee cups in the scene. Robin's hand was shaking just as much as hers. "I felt better to see that he was as out of control as I was," she laughs. Of course, now that one season has passed, Robin and Pam aren't scared anymore. They give each other a lot of support, and Pam has learned a lot about improvisational acting from Robin, who thrives on breaking into unexpected routines and making up lines as the show goes along.

Off the set, Pam is a loner. She lives in a house in the Hollywood Hills and drives a Volkswagen convertible to and from the studio. She recently bought a cabin in upstate New York where she goes during time off to relax. "I developed a love for outdoor things early in life. I have a wood stove in my cabin and I can cook natural foods and bake bread," she beams.

Besides acting, Pam is planning on a singing career, and has the lead in a new movie for television, *Haywire*. Both Robin and Pam are talented enough to carry on with their careers long after *Mork and Mindy* is remembered as an "oldie-but-goodie." Of course, with the gigantic following the show has, it could be around for — a bleem!

# Shelley Hack: Charlie's Newest Angel!

First is was Farrah. Then it was Kate Jackson. One by one the original "Charlie's Angels" are leaving the show. Farrah caused quite an uproar when she left, because she broke her contract. No one worried for long, because Cheryl Ladd came along and easily filled Farrah's shoes (or should we say wings?).

When it became known that Kate Jackson would not be returning to the show next season, the first question was, "Why? Did she quit or was she fired?" Amidst conflicting stories, Kate admitted, "I guess I did cause a few problems. What it comes down to is I got tired of them and they got tired of me. I'm glad I've finally been able to hang up the halo."

Apparently it was a mutual decision, and producers Leonard Goldberg and Aaron Spelling said, "Due to problems on the set, Kate's being dropped for the good of the show." Immediately after this announcement, everyone began to wonder who the next Angel would be. The producers wondered too, as they auditioned thousands of beautiful girls in their nationwide search.

The newest angel is blonde, beautiful Shelley Hack, a 31-year-old model and actress from Greenwich, Connecticut. Appropriately enough, Shelley was the "Charlie" girl in the Revlon perfume commercials, but she's also had several small roles in television and theatrical movies, including *Annie Hall* and *If Ever I See You Again*.

Producer Aaron Spelling said, "Frankly, Kate was not easy to replace. She was terrific in the show — she had just the right image. Most of the girls we saw were gorgeous, but they didn't have the right bubble and intelligence."

"Shelley is a very bright lady," said Goldberg. "And she was totally and instantly likable in the tests. We shot film of her with Jackie and Cheryl before making our final decision, and it looked good. They both called to say they liked her and felt comfortable with her."

Off stage Shelley is bright and intelligent, too. She graduated from Smith College, then attended the University of Sydney in Australia and studied archeology. She got her first modeling job when she was 15.

On the show, Shelley plays investigator Tiffany Welles, the daughter of a Connecticut police chief who is an old buddy of Charlie, the Angels' unseen boss. With six years of acting classes behind her, Shelley is looking forward to doing more on *Charlie's Angels* than just smiling and looking pretty. She's thrilled about her new career, and her new friends. Jaclyn Smith, Cheryl Ladd, and Shelley make a terrific threesome — the ratings prove it!

**Charlie's newest angel is beautiful Shelley Hack. If you've seen a commercial for a particular brand of perfume, then you may have seen Shelley before her television acting debut.**

# Meet John Schneider: He's a Prince of a Duke

Interviewing John Schneider, who stars as Bo Duke on *The Dukes of Hazzard*, is not only interesting, it's fun! He's sincere, bright, and outgoing. As he talks, he looks directly at you, and he puts you immediately at ease.

**Q:** *How did you get the role of Bo Duke?*

**John:** Actually, it wasn't hard at all. When I went to the audition, I was already playing the part of Bo. I borrowed an old pickup truck, put on a funky hat, and arrived at the producer's office in Atlanta without shaving. I probably looked horrible, but I put my feet up on the desk, did my country accent, and told them I came from Snailville, although there's no such place.

I was born in Mount Kisco, New York, and my parents were divorced when I was about two years old. When I was fourteen, my mother took me to live in Atlanta, Georgia, where she had taken a job. I became involved in the city's community theaters practically the moment I stepped off the plane. I love entertaining people more than anything.

As a kid, I learned magic because it was another way I could entertain. The magic book said, "This trick takes two years to learn," but I knew I could pick it up right away, and I did.

**Q:** *Did you study other things, too?*

**John:** Yes, a few things. I even attended the Georgia School of High Performance Driving when I was sixteen to learn to race-drive, just in case I was up for a part in a movie or something where they needed a driver. And they did in *The Dukes of Hazzard*!

Most of the stunt driving is done by me and my co-star, Tom Wopat. He's a real stunt driver. We have a lot of fun messing around with "General Lee," the car we drive in the show, even when the cameras aren't rolling.

**Q:** *What other hobbies do you have?*

**John:** Well, I love playing the guitar and singing. I taught myself how to play. As a teenager, I entertained at Atlanta clubs and at private parties with an act made up of magic, a little conversation, guitar music, and songs I wrote. I

17

**John Schneider and Tom Wopat enjoy working with lovely Catherine Bach on *The Dukes of Hazzard*.**

was always going to be a singer, but then I tried acting and liked it even more. Besides the TV series, I've been in a couple of films — with Burt Reynolds and Sally Field in *Smokey and the Bandit,* and in *Million Dollar Dixie Deliverance.*

**Q:** *Do you get a lot of fan mail?*

**John:** I get about twenty-five hundred letters a week at the studio. It's marvelous. I think fans should be treated with love. I want to be somebody who's loved as much as Elvis, yet be able to walk down the street and not be mobbed. Fans know you are a person and treat you that way if you are that way. It's important to remain yourself and not let stardom affect you. I hate fakiness in actors — in people. I always want to be real.

**Q:** *What is the one thing you like best about show business?*

**John:** Aside from entertaining people, I love the people I've been able to work with. They're wonderful. My co-stars and the crew are like a family. It's not like work, but more like you go to be with your friends and you just happen to be filming at the same time.

**Q:** *What do you like the least?*

**John:** About show business? I don't really have any complaints. It's what I always wanted to do, and I'm doing it.

**Q:** *How does your mother feel about your success?*

**John:** She loves it. She's gone crazy. She's my biggest fan and always has been. She never doubted that I'd make it and she's always been proud of me and my accomplishments. In fact, she's the main reason I really stuck with it through the years. She went to every rehearsal, every show, every opening night. Last Christmas I was making enough money from the show to buy her something extra special — a real nice, fur-lined leather coat. It was a good feeling to be able to give her that.

**Q:** *What kind of qualities do you look for in a girl?*

**John:** Sincerity. That's very important. And someone who isn't all that excited about my being an actor. Someone who likes me for myself.

**Q:** *What kind of dates do you enjoy most?*

**John:** I like to go to the mountains. Just two people on a picnic. Maybe where there's a lake and a nice waterfall for swimming and picnicking. You know, take along some turkey or chicken and soda. And lots of ice cream — I love it. Or if you can't have an outdoor date, I like a nice restaurant with a fire, then going for a drive.

**Q:** *Do you have a personal philosophy about life?*

**John:** Yes — stay happy and make people happy. That's about it. Try to help people. People really count.

# Valerie Bertinelli: She Takes Life *One Day at a Time*

When Valerie Bertinelli began working four years ago on *One Day at a Time* as Barbara Cooper, she was a lot like the carefree, wise-cracking character she played.

But today, at 19, Valerie has really changed, and so has her TV character. "I really grew up on *One Day at a Time*," she says. "And while I was growing I had two wonderful families watching over me."

She's talking, of course, about her real family and her TV family. "Maybe it's just a make-believe family," she says about the Cooper/Romanos, "but I spend a lot of time with my co-stars on the set each week. We share problems, talk a lot, laugh together. During the day when I wasn't with my real family, they were all there."

Val (or Bert, as her friends call her) is just as close to her real family — her parents and three brothers (two younger and one older). Recently, she bought a house of her own. She felt terrified at the thought of plunging into her own life, but it was exciting, too.

Valerie didn't always want to be an actress. As a child in Delaware, Michigan, she saw herself as an airline stewardess or hair stylist. But

A very grown-up and glamorous Valerie attracts attention wherever she goes.

when her family moved to California, 11-year-old Val, who was very shy, decided she'd like to give acting a try. Going to acting classes and to auditions for commercials might help her overcome her shyness.

It wasn't long before Val won parts in several commercials, and "seeing myself on the screen really made me want to be an actress even more," she recalls. Three years later she won the role of Barbara. At first, because of her lack of real acting experience, Val's part on *One Day at a Time* wasn't as large as she hoped it would be. But as the months passed and her hours in acting class began to show, she was given more and more to do on the show, until some of the scripts were written entirely around her.

Before she turned 18, Val, like all working minors, could work only four hours a day, and had to go to school three hours a day on the set. She would get up about seven A.M., drive with her mother to the studio, work, go to school, go home, study both her schoolwork and her lines for the next day, and go to bed.

While the show was on its annual break, she was able to attend public school. "It was sort of hard to adjust to being in a regular school after being tutored on the set. I always had to make a special effort to convince the kids that I was still the same old me," she recalls.

Val feels that the show is very realistic. "I've

never lived in a 'divorce situation,' but people who have tell me it's very much like the way we present it on our show. I think lots of people enjoy seeing true-to-life incidents made funny — especially kids and women who are living through that sort of experience. Some of our material has been very controversial, but that's what *One Day* is all about — showing the way things really are."

Because her show films before a live audience, Val has finally lost most of her shyness. "It's lots of fun," she declares. "When we flub a line and have to stop the cameras and start over, the audience loves it."

Besides being a very popular young actress on TV, Val's starring in a new motion picture, *C.H.O.M.P.S.* The movie is about a bionic dog. Well, there are *worse* co-stars!

A great deal of her fan mail is from girls who'd like to know how to get where Val is today. "They think it happens overnight," she sighs, "but it isn't that easy. Acting is a lot of hard work, and I'm working even harder to be good enough to do all sorts of parts, including musical ones. I take singing, dancing, and piano, too. The most important thing is to think things through and know what you really want to do with your life, then head in that direction. We all have to do what we think is best for ourselves, and take things one day at a time."

# *CHiPs:*
# Back on the Road

Every week on *CHiPs*, television's hit series, Erik Estrada and his co-star, Larry Wilcox, zoom up and down the freeways of Southern California on their Kawasaki 900 motorcycles. Erik and Larry portray young California Highway Patrol motorcycle officers, Francis "Ponch" Poncherello and Jonathan Baker. To watch them weave in and out of traffic, you'd think they'd been riding motorcycles all their lives, but they haven't.

Before Erik was in *CHiPs*, he admits he had never even been on a motorcycle before. "I had to take special lessons for six weeks, learning how to turn, clutch, brake, and coordinate the throttle. Physically, it was the most exhausting thing I've ever done," he says.

"If you don't learn to sit properly, you can hurt your back. Even after the first week on the bike my legs, calves, and thighs were sore from all the braking, shifting, and jerking around. I didn't realize all the tension that builds up!"

Luckily, Erik had been working out at a local gym for several years, so he developed a lot of stamina. It really came in handy during those six weeks of bike lessons.

Erik still works to keep his body in top shape. "Being in *CHiPs* is long, hard work," he says, "and I've got to be in the best shape I can be." Erik also gulps down loads of vitamins, wheat germ oil, liver extract, and kelp!

Erik's body-building includes karate. He practices daily with his instructor, Frank Argelander, who is a black belt. Each morning, Frank comes to Erik's house to give him a two-hour workout that would stagger a Marine! First, there is a short warmup period, then they jog around the park a couple of times. Then, they head for home where they do 240 situps, 120 pushups, 40 leg raises, and more! Finally, Frank and Erik really work out, going through all the strenuous feats involved in karate!

Erik lives in an elegant townhouse not too far from the TV studio. It is filled with antiques, modern Italian furniture, plants, and two dogs — a German shepherd named "Don't Cry," and a small white terrier Erik affectionately named "Killer."

Erik admits that at one point in his life, when he was a young boy growing up in New York's Spanish Harlem, he had planned on becoming a policeman. "I never figured I'd be *acting* the part," he says today. In fact, Erik stumbled into an acting career by accident. He joined the high school drama club in hopes of meeting a girl he had his eyes on. He won a part in the school play, and quickly got hooked on acting.

After high school, Erik joined a cultural drama program and performed for 32 weeks in a variety of plays in the city's parks. Then he enrolled at the American Musical Dramatic Academy for a couple of years. His first show-business break came when he was signed to co-star in the film *The Cross and the Switchblade*.

Then it was back to acting school, and earning money by waiting on tables while he waited for a role to come along. It did in the hit movie, *The New Centurions*, in which he played a Spanish-American rookie policeman.

Erik and his co-star Larry Wilcox have become the best of friends during the two seasons that *CHiPs* has been on the air. The two make quite a contrast on the screen, and perhaps that's part of their appeal. Erik is the tall, dark,

Erik is a real animal lover, and adopted "Don't Cry" (part German shepherd) when he found him wandering around lost and homeless. He got "Killer" to keep "Don't Cry" company when he's busy at work all day.

and handsome "Romeo," and Larry is blond, blue-eyed — a real family man. Larry has been married to Judy Nagner for several years, and has a son, Derek, 10 years old, and a daughter, Heidi, five.

More at home on a horse than a motorcycle, Larry, too, had to spend several weeks learning how to properly ride a big bike. "Motorcycles are much more dangerous than horses," he says, even though "I spend a lot of my free time going to rodeos, roping, and riding. I love it.

Rodeo people are natural and honest, and the roping exhilarates me. The horse is running full blast and I'm trying to conquer the steer and the horse at the same time. It makes me feel free!"

When he's not riding, Larry pursues a wide range of interests, including breeding Arabian horses, writing screenplays, and playing the guitar and piano.

The *CHiPs* shows this season will range from gas-shortage problems to young guys cruising the streets — and there will be something extra, too. Erik Estrada will be singing the new theme song every week!

*EDITOR'S NOTE: Just as this book was being printed we learned of Erik's terrible motorcycle accident, an accident which might have been worse. However, as is obvious by now, Erik is mending from his injuries and will be shown on CHiPs to be recovering from an accident that Ponch has had! Of course, since Erik really is recuperating, a stand-in will have to be used to film the "fake" accident. Let's hope Erik is up and around very soon!*

# *BJ and the Bear*'s Greg Evigan

How does it feel to have a chimpanzee for a co-star? Greg Evigan, who stars as Billie Joe McKay on *BJ and the Bear*, loves it! "Chimps don't mind if they don't have as many lines as you do," he jokes.

Seriously, Greg and his chimp friend, Sam, have become good buddies while working to make their series a hit. "Animals can tell if you don't like them, or if you're just pretending," Greg says. He definitely doesn't have that problem with Sam, who stars as Bear, his best friend and front-seat companion when he rides the highways of America as an independent trucker.

It wasn't hard for Greg to like Sam. He's

**Greg Evigan and his TV partner, Bear (whose real name is Sam), have a good working relationship on the *BJ* set.**

always been an animal lover. At home he has a dog named Chewy and a cat called Maurice, "plus a lot of friends from the neighborhood that come and visit, like Fred the squirrel and a bluejay."

It's quite a change from the way he grew up in New Jersey, and Greg says he's definitely been Californian-ized. "The weather makes it so great," he smiles. "Just being able to go out whenever you want without asking, 'Do you think it will rain?' is terrific."

31

The one thing Greg does miss about New Jersey is his family. He grew up in a close family atmosphere with lots of relatives. "We always had big get-togethers with good food and music."

Music has always been a big interest of Greg's. He plays the piano, drums, flute, and saxophone — and sings, too. In fact, Greg originally wanted to be a bandleader. When he was graduated from high school he didn't have a particular goal in mind. He had taken a couple of acting classes at school and was part of the drama club. But he hadn't thought seriously about becoming an actor until he took a trip to New York. There he saw a sign for open auditions for a musical called *Jesus Christ Superstar*. Greg had to audition 15 times before he got the role and he says he was scared to death. "I didn't know anything compared to the other people trying out, but I listened and watched, and somehow pulled it off!"

Greg toured with the play across the United States. He also played for a year on Broadway. Then he came to Hollywood to star in a new series, *Year at the Top*. That show had a very short run, but it made a lot of people aware of his talent and charm. Today he's Billie Joe McKay, trucking down the highway on *BJ and the Bear*.

# *Three's* Still Good Company

Seems like everyone enjoys the company of Joyce DeWitt, Suzanne Somers, and John Ritter in television's popular situation comedy *Three's Company*. The charm and appeal of each star is more than tripled in each other's company.

Pretty and pouty Suzanne, who plays Chrissy, is intelligent and talented in many ways. This young actress has already published two books of poetry. Suzanne believes that "You can be whatever you want to be. There's an area in our subconscious mind that responds to our dreams and desires if we sincerely try." She is so convinced of this that she has recently written a book called *Some People Live More*

*Than Others*, about how people can get the most out of their lives. It's a self-help book designed to get people to improve their individual selves.

Although Suzanne seems perfectly content with her life and successful television career, she has at least two more goals in mind: to write a cookbook and to sing in a Broadway musical! Knowing Suzanne, she'll eventually do them both — and more!

Like his character, Jack, on *Three's Company*, John Ritter used to have a reputation for going after the girls. Then, four years ago, he met his wife, Nancy, and from that day on he's become a one-woman man. A natural ham, John is very good at relaxing the cast during breaks. He manages to keep everyone in good spirits during the long shooting schedules by acting silly and clowning around. John says that during the first season on his show he was very nervous. "It felt so unreal to be involved in a weekly show," he admits, "and I thought I'd freak out." That made John stop and think about the important things in life. "The thing to do is keep a light head and a degree of concentration and don't make stardom any bigger than it really is or it will tear you apart."

Joyce DeWitt rounds out the talented *Three's Company* cast. Although she admits that being an actress is hectic, she wouldn't have it any other way. She's usually up before eight, feeds

**The cast of *Three's Company:* John Ritter, surrounded by Suzanne Somers and Joyce DeWitt.**

her dog, meditates for 15 minutes, gulps down her orange juice and muffin, and begins the 45-minute drive to the studio.

"I once tried driving to work and eating breakfast at the same time," Joyce laughs, "but the back of my car got filled with spoons, napkins, and plates, and looked terrible."

Joyce feels one of the greatest things about having a hit series is all the friends she's made. "Fans are wonderful," she says. "I'm really thrilled with all the letters I get from our viewers. Our fans are very special to me, and I want them to know that!"

# Peter Barton: A "New" Son for Shirley Jones

Peter Thomas Barton has started off in show business with a bang. He stars in the NBC series, *Shirley*, as the son of Shirley Jones. Everybody knows raising a family just isn't easy, especially when you've got to do it all by yourself. Shirley Jones plays Shirley Miller, a woman who realizes her late husband's dream to leave the hectic life of the big city. So, she packs up her family and moves to Lake Tahoe, California, for a new beginning.

Peter plays Shirley's oldest son, Billy, and like most 17-year-olds, he's got plenty of girl problems. Ten-year-old Bret Shryer plays Peter's brother, Hemm, and Tracey Gold Claire stars as their sister, Michelle.

Now that filming on the series has begun on a weekly basis, Peter says he's discovered how little free time he has. He arrives on the set by six A.M. and usually finishes at the same time — six P.M. "Then I get home about seven P.M., grab a bite to eat, study my lines for the next day, and hit the sack," Peter sighs. Sure, it's a rough schedule, but he wouldn't trade it for anything.

*Shirley* is Peter's first television acting role, although he has done some stage work. Before moving to California for his role, he earned money as a top male fashion model. Originally from New York, 20-year-old Peter says what he misses most about his hometown is not being close to his family. In real life, he also has a brother and a sister; their names are Billy and Linda.

To prepare for his role as Billy Miller, Peter took acting classes for about six hours a day. He started when he found out he had won the role and continued until filming began — about three months.

"Everything outdoors," is Peter's answer if you ask him what he likes best in life. Besides scuba diving, working out with weights, jogging, and playing a little tennis, he loves flying, and even has a pilot's license. Indoors, he enjoys playing the piano, cooking, and spending time with the new friends he's made in Hollywood.

Peter's a health-food nut, and one of the specialties he enjoys cooking is bran muffins. "I'm not a gourmet chef or anything like that," he laughs, "but I do all right in the kitchen."

Born on July 19, 1959, Peter stands an even six feet tall, weighs about 150 pounds, and has brown hair and hazel eyes. His favorite performers are Humphrey Bogart and Bette Davis, and if he's going to listen to music, you can bet the Bee Gees will be included in his selection.

Handsome Peter Barton was a model before he became an actor.

Working on *Shirley* five days a week doesn't give Peter much free time, but, he says, "At least I don't have to worry about giving up a social life — I don't have one, anyway."

"Impossible!" you say? How could anyone so handsome, talented, and available not have a social life?

Peter says it's easy. When he moved out to Los Angeles from New York to get settled, he didn't know anybody in town. Since then he's made a few friends, but he did leave all his "grew-up-together" buddies behind. "I was very lonely at first," he confesses. "I felt like a kid lost in the big city."

Working with Shirley Jones on the series is a real treat for Peter, and quite a learning experience, too. "Just watching her work, listening to her, and asking for advice has helped me tremendously," Peter says. "I couldn't think of anyone else I'd rather be working with."

Speaking of Shirley Jones, you probably remember her as Shirley Partridge of *The Partridge Family*, a TV show now in reruns. Mrs. Partridge was also a widow with a teenage son. He was played by her actual stepson, David Cassidy, who was tremendously popular for a few years.

And, of course, her son Shaun Cassidy was one of the Hardy boys in the series of the same name. He has since starred in a TV movie, *Like*

*Normal People*, besides having a successful singing career. There are two more Cassidy boys at home waiting in the wings. Patrick is 17, and Ryan is 14.

Shirley Jones' new series keeps her busy, but she makes sure she's home every night for dinner with her real family. "It's important for young people to have a family feeling," Shirley believes, and she's never let her successful show-business career make her a stranger to her children.

Shirley's TV daughter Michelle is played by Tracey Gold Claire, who has quite a list of credits for a 10-year-old. She's been very busy in commercials, had a role in *Roots*, and starred in two TV movies, *The Incredible Journey of Dr. Meg Laurel* with Lindsay Wagner, and *The Child Stealers* with Beau Bridges. She's also been featured on episodes of *Quincy*, *Fantasy Island*, and *CHiPs*.

Although she attends public school when not working, Tracey is taught by a tutor while on the set. As a minor, she's only allowed to work four hours a day, so she spends the rest of her time in class, or roller skating around the studio lot. She also enjoys swimming and writing stories.

Bret Daniel Shryer plays Hemm Miller on *Shirley*, and says confidently, "I expected to get the part, and I did." This marks his first theatrical role, although you may have seen him before in many commercials. Like Tracey, Bret is tutored on the set and is quite a good student. After studying, he likes to toss around a baseball or play touch-football with the rest of the cast and crew. Plus, he's a whiz on a skateboard.

Together, Shirley Jones, Peter, Bret, and Tracey make a terrific television family, as you've probably seen for yourself.

# Gary Coleman: *Diff'rent Strokes* Is for All Folks!

*Diff'rent Strokes* is a special kind of television show, and its star, Gary Coleman, is the chief reason why. He shares the spotlight with Todd Bridges, Dana Plato, Charlotte Rae, and the head of the family himself, Conrad Bain, but it's Gary who gives the show that something extra.

With his chipmunk cheeks, button eyes, and a voice that doesn't seem to fit his barely four-foot-high frame, Gary captures attention both on and off camera. When he speaks, he moves his hands, rolls his eyes, and talks with facial expressions as well — and he is definitely not camera-shy!

Says Gary, "Why should I be afraid of the camera? If it wore a black cape and had fangs,

I'd be scared of it, but since it doesn't, why be afraid?"

Gary's swift rise to stardom was no surprise to his mother. She says she always knew Gary had a special gift. Gary, however, almost didn't get to share his gift with the world. At the age of two, he was stricken with a chronic kidney disease. By the time he was five, surgeons had removed one useless kidney and the other was getting worse by the day. Finally, in 1974, he received a kidney transplant, and since then he's been making up for all those months he spent in and out of hospitals.

The kidney disease affected Gary's growth, which explains why when *Diff'rent Strokes* began, Gary, at age 10, was about the size of a normal five-year-old. But his small frame and pudgy cheeks are the only noticeable signs of his illness. He has energy to burn as he races around the set.

Gary's career began a few years ago when he started modeling and doing commercials. Then, he auditioned for a role in a new, updated version of *The Little Rascals*, and was chosen to play the part of Stymie (Stoker in the new version). The show was never aired. But, when *Diff'rent Strokes* came along, the producers remembered Gary, and the part of Arnold went to him.

Gary and his co-star, Todd Bridges, who

plays Willis, have formed a deep friendship over the last year. On the set they play hide-and-seek, wrestle, ride skateboards, and study together with a tutor. And, although their characters on the show are different, Gary and Todd are pretty much alike off camera. They're both bright, energetic, independent, and very talented.

Todd says his character, Willis, "is a good character for black kids (and all children) to relate to because he loves his little brother and

Conrad Bain, who plays Phillip Drummond, a Park Avenue millionaire, embraces Todd Bridges, who plays Willis, and Gary Coleman, who plays Arnold, the two youngsters he has adopted in the NBC-TV comedy series, *Diff'rent Strokes*.

wants to take care of him." He adds that there is a lot of responsibility in the role "because Willis is the older brother. Sometimes he's mean, sometimes he's nice, and sometimes he's in the middle. Just like it is with most brothers," he laughs.

Todd's interests outside of acting are science, sports, and snakes — which he often finds in the hills surrounding his home. "I love catching king snakes and gopher snakes. They come out in my backyard and I grab 'em."

While Todd's busy with his snakes, Gary prefers his model trains. He's invested more than $9,000 in his hobby. "There's a natural beauty and sleekness trains have that I like. They keep things moving. I like the switches, the lights, tracks — everything."

According to their parents, Todd and Gary are just normal children who happen to be in show business. Working on a series is hard work, but they find plenty of time for friends and fun. Asked if he plans to make acting his lifelong career, Gary replies: "No, not really. I may take acting as a part-time job and do something else." His fans certainly hope not!

# *The Bad News Bears* Are Good News, and Here's the Starting Lineup

Everyone thought it was good news when the hit movie *The Bad News Bears* was developed as a series for television. Even better news was *Bad News* turned out to be so successful that the series was renewed for this year. Those guys (and one girl!) who hit the ball (or miss it!) and find ways of getting in and out of trouble each week are played by some very talented young people. And here they are:

*Shane Butterworth:* He's almost 10 years old and is a native Californian who loves all sports, but says football, ice skating, and baseball are his favorites. If you think you've seen him before on television, you're right. He's done guest appearances on shows such as *Laverne and Shirley*, *Lou Grant*, *Quincy*, and *Nancy Drew*, as well as commercials. On *Bears*, he plays number 8, Lupus, and says this show is the most fun he's ever had in acting.

*Corey Feldman:* *Love Boat*, *Eight Is Enough*, and *Alice* are just three of the hit television shows Corey's appeared on in his acting career. He's only eight, but he's crammed more show business into his life than people twice his age. His mom's a dancer, his dad's a rock musician, so how can he help but be talented? As Reggie on the show, Corey sports a number 6 on his jersey, and made his acting debut in a McDonald's commercial.

*Gregg Forest:* As Kelly, Gregg is the oldest player on the *Bears* team, and this is his first role on a TV series. He was born in Los Angeles, California, and has been featured in many commercials. He also guest starred on *Happy Days*, *Little House on the Prairie*, and *CHiPs*. Does he mind having to go to work every day to film? "No. How can playing ball be work?" he asks.

*Billy Jacoby:* He's definitely not a newcomer to acting — he comes from a show-business family. His older brother, Scott, is a fine actor himself, and Billy starred with Scott in the award-winning TV movie, *That Certain Summer*. Billy was just three years old at the time, and since then he's appeared on several television shows and on stage with Debbie Reynolds in *Annie Get Your Gun*. He's also co-starred in two feature films: *The Runner Stumbles* and, most recently, *Sunnyside*, with John Travolta's brother, Joey. He's Bear number 9 — Rudi Stein.

*Christoff St. John:* Thirteen-year-old Christoff was "born in a trunk." That's a show-business term which means you were born into a show-business family. His dad is an actor, writer, and director, and his mom is an actress and singer. Christoff says his most impressive role was playing the part of young Alex Haley in Part 2 of *Roots*. A singer and guitarist as well as an actor, Christoff also loves baseball, swimming, horseback riding — and answering fan mail!

*Sparky Marcus:* Acting is fun, but Sparky really loves playing golf and baseball, and skateboarding. He describes himself as "a regular kind of guy," but this 11-year-old made his show-business debut at the age of five. Later, he won roles in *WKRP in Cincinnati* and *What's Happening!!* He co-starred in the series *Mary Hartman, Mary Hartman* and *Grandpa Goes to Washington*.

Jack Warden, who plays the team's coach, keeps the
Bears hard at work, practicing for the big games ahead.

*Tricia Cast*: The prettiest member of the
baseball team is Tricia Cast, who plays
Amanda. She was born in Medford, New York,
on November 16th, and will soon be 14. The
very first time she saw a play, she knew acting
was for her. She likes school, too, and is an
honor student. How does she spend her free
time? Writing plays.

*J. Brenner Smith*: Englebert, the Bears' number 15, is one of the younger members of the cast. Blue-eyed, with brown hair, J. is a nine-year-old native Californian. His acting career began in a Fritos commercial. He attends school on the set with his co-stars, but when he's not filming, he likes to go to public school. He lists ice skating, baseball, and acting as his favorite things, and says *The Bad News Bears* is the best thing to happen to him so far in his life!

*Meeno Peluce*: Meeno was born in Holland on February 26, 1970, and plays number 2, Tanner. During the first years of his life, his family traveled all over the world, so the acting bug didn't really bite him until he reached the ripe age of four. Meeno appears in the film *The Amityville Horror*, and he loved being a guest star on shows such as *The Incredible Hulk* and *Starsky and Hutch*. He was also in the TV movies *Loose Change* and *The Ghost of Flight 401*.

# Gil Gerard:
# Buck Rogers Is His
# Dream Come True!

Did you know that Buck Rogers has been around for over 50 years? He made his first appearance in 1929 as a popular comic-strip character, when the idea of sending a rocket through space was still just a fantasy.

Buck Rogers was America's first popular space hero, long before Luke Skywalker and R2D2 captured the hearts of people everywhere in *Star Wars*. Now, in *Buck Rogers in the 25th Century*, Buck shows us a look at our world, five centuries from now, with a lot of fun, mischief, and adventure.

Based on the recent movie, the show is about an astronaut who finds himself suddenly living in the future. There, life is concentrated in one

enormous city surrounded by a deserted waste-
land filled with criminals and scary creatures.

As played by actor Gil Gerard, Buck is a
fun-loving guy who refuses to take life seriously. During a grand and elegant ball, where
his friends are doing a very formalized waltz to
computer-programmed music, he teaches
everyone to disco!

Gil became very well known because of his hit
film, *Buck Rogers in the 25th Century*, but he
started his career in commercials. He also spent
two years playing a doctor in TV's daytime soap
opera *The Doctors*.

**Gil Gerard really looks pretty far out in his Buck
Rogers costume.**

Still, he admits that his success seems like a dream. He wasn't always interested in acting. In fact, in his native Arkansas, he was the vice-president of a chemical firm and an advisor to the governor. Then, one day, Gil heard the song "Is That All There Is?" and "something hit me between the eyes. I realized that playing golf and doing the work I was doing were not what I wanted for the rest of my life."

So, Gil quit his high-paying job and moved to New York. He studied acting by day and drove a cab by night. An invitation from a passenger to work as an extra in the film *Love Story* launched his career.

In person, Gil is very much like Buck Rogers. He's got a wonderful sense of humor, enjoys lots of action, and is a real charmer with the ladies. Because the hour-long show uses many special effects, the filming schedule is long and hard. Still, Gil says he wouldn't have it any other way. Starring as Buck Rogers is a boy's dream come true!

# TV Questions and Answers

All the questions — and answers — about your favorite television shows, characters, stars, and more!

**Q:** I would like to know how long the show *The Big Blue Marble* has been on TV, and if it is shown outside the United States?
**A:** The show that tells how all sorts of kids live, work, and play has been on TV since 1974. It is currently seen on about 200 stations in the U.S. and in 70 nations abroad.

**Q:** I really like to watch *The Battle of the Network Stars*. I was wondering if the stars

**Mackenzie Phillips, co-star of *One Day at a Time*, loves participating in *The Battle of the Network Stars* sports competitions.**

have to practice for the sports or are they picked because they are already pretty good?
**A:** Some of the stars on the show are already very accomplished in their particular sport, while others must practice for several weeks. However, an amateur would be picked to compete against another amateur and a star who was better would be picked to compete against a star who is his equal.

**Q:** One of my favorite actors on TV is Michael Landon. What did he do before starring in *The Little House on the Prairie?*

**A:** Michael has written and directed several episodes of *Little House* and has also worked on a few TV movies. You have also probably seen him on the Kodak camera commercials. Before that, he was one of the stars of *Bonanza*, a Western.

**Q:** Is there anything on TV for kids that is like the *60 Minutes* show for adults? I really like to know what's happening in the world but I just can't get interested in the regular news shows.

**A:** Several TV news shows for youths are broadcast on weekends. For example, *Youth and the Issues* is on early Sunday mornings in some cities. *The Big Blue Marble* has a news segment, "In the News." Check listings for time and channels.

**Q:** Every year I see a listing for a *Special Olympics* show. Although I've never watched one, I wonder what is so special about it. Is it a special show about the Olympic games?

**A:** The *Special Olympics* is like the Olympic games except the players are mentally or physically handicapped.

**Q:** Do stars get paid for being on TV talk shows?

**A:** No. Most stars like the publicity the shows bring, especially if they are promoting a new book, televison series, or movie.

**Q:** I love to watch some of the TV game shows, and I always dream about being on one when I'm older. How do people get on the shows?

**A:** The next time you watch a show, pay attention at the end. There will usually be an

Here is the cast of *Eight Is Enough* winning a special *Family Feud* game.

announcer who tells where to write for tickets
to watch or appear on the show. The age limit
for contestants on most game shows is 18, but
you can write to the show for information.

**Q:** Do the actors in soap operas ever make up
a line if they forget theirs?

**A:** It depends on the situation. Sometimes an
actor will "ad-lib" a line if he/she forgets or
misses one. Many actors ad-lib to keep a show
rolling.

**Q:** *The Incredible Hulk* is one of my favorite
shows. I would like to know the names of other
shows Bill Bixby has starred in.

**A:** Bixby, who plays the part of David Banner, was in *The Courtship of Eddie's Father*,
*My Favorite Martian*, and *The Magician*. The
shows are sometimes shown as reruns on vari-
ous stations.

**Q:** Many times a new TV movie will be re-
viewed in the newspaper before it's been on.
How can a movie be reviewed if it hasn't been on
TV yet?

**A:** New movies are "previewed" by newspaper and television reviewers at special show-
ings of the movie.

**Q:** Can you please explain what PBS is? I know that it is the channel for shows like *Sesame Street* and *Electric Company*.

**A:** The initials PBS stand for Public Broadcasting System. The station uses money donated by the public to show the programs. PBS is also known as educational television because the shows may be education-oriented as well as entertaining. Since that station operates on public money, there are no sponsors and, therefore, no commercials.

**Q:** I think *Gilligan's Island* reruns are really fun to watch. What island was it filmed on?

**A:** The "island" was really a stage set at Universal Studios, in Hollywood, California. If you go on a tour of the studio, you can see where the show was filmed.

**Q:** I've noticed in a lot of shows where there is pie throwing that the actors don't lick the pie off their faces? Why?

**A:** Shaving-cream pies don't taste very good!

**Q:** Why is it that some actors "die" on series that have been on for a long time?

**A:** Sometimes when a character on a show "dies," it is because the actor decided not to be in the series anymore. If the character is supposed to just move away, then he or she can always come back for a guest appearance.

**Q:** Why did *The Donny and Marie Show* become *The Osmond Family Show?* Did Donny and Marie get tired of doing all the work?
**A:** Donny and Marie decided they wanted the rest of their family to share in the fun and work of filming a TV show, but it has since been cancelled.

**Q:** *Eight Is Enough* is one of the best shows on TV. I heard that the man who plays the father might not be back on the show. Is this true?
**A:** As this was being written, Dick Van Patten was asking the producers for more money per episode. However, the show does so well in the ratings, it is expected that a new contract will be worked out.

**Q:** Is it true that the woman who plays Laverne on *Laverne and Shirley* is married to the man who played Mike on *All in the Family*?

As Laverne and Shirley, Penny Marshall and Cindy
Williams are always up to something — even showing
off their dancing talent with Lenny (Michael McKean)
and Squiggy (David Lander).

**A:** Yes. Rob Reiner and Penny Marshall are
married. They lived across the street from each
other when they were growing up.

**Q:** I don't understand the *$1.98 Beauty Show.*
Why is it that some of the girls don't even seem
like beauty queens?
**A:** The show is a satire on beauty pageants
and is meant to be humorous.

**Q:**   Why is it that most of the TV commercials shown during morning and afternoon weekend programs are for cereals and candy?

**A:**   Sponsors of these shows push the products they feel will most likely appeal to their audience, which, at these hours, is mostly kids.

**Q:**   This may sound like a silly question, but how do the TV stars know what to say during the show?

**A:**   The actors and actresses get their lines from a script written by a TV writer. The script tells each person *what* to say and *when* to say it. It's up to the director and the shows' stars just *how* the lines are said. Usually the actors memorize all the lines before filming begins.

**Q:**   What is the difference between a regular movie and a TV movie?

**A:**   A TV movie is one made just to be shown on television. A regular movie, or "feature" film, is a movie first shown in theaters. Often, a feature film is eventually broadcast on television. When that happens, the film sometimes must be edited (have parts taken out) to allow time for commercial breaks.

**Q:** Do you have to be a great dancer to appear on shows like *Soul Train* or *American Bandstand*?

**A:** You don't necessarily have to be a great dancer, but it helps. The best way to find out what the requirements are for appearing on a show is to write to the producers. Often the address is shown at the end of the program.

**Q:** Do the men on *Taxi* really know how to drive taxi cabs?

**A:** Well, since taxis aren't any different to drive than regular cars, they probably could. But they're too busy with acting careers to try driving taxis—and that goes for Marilu Henner (the female taxi driver), too!

Andy Kaufman stars on *Taxi* as Latka Graves, a mechanic who's as funny on screen as Andy is off screen.

**Q:** Who is the little girl who played the part of Barbara's daughter in *My Three Sons*?

**A:** Dawn Lynn, at 16, isn't a little girl anymore. Did you know that she is the sister of teen singer Leif Garrett?

**Q:** I think *Maude* was a really neat show. I liked her because she always seemed to stand up for what she believed in. Can you tell me how this show came about?

**A:** Maude was a character from *All in the Family*. On the show, she was Edith Bunker's cousin from New York. She got a show of her own when she became very popular.

**Q:** Why is it that some of my favorite shows go off the air? I used to love *Star Trek*, *Wonder Woman*, *The Bionic Woman*, and *The Six Million Dollar Man*.

**A:** Shows are taken off the air because they don't get high enough ratings. What that means is that not many people were interested enough to watch the show.

**Q:** *Mayberry R.F.D.* makes me laugh. I really like the man who plays the part of Sam. Who is he?

**A:** Ken Berry. You may have spotted him on some shoe commercials.

**Q:** On his show *Lou Grant*, is Edward Asner supposed to be the same character he created on *The Mary Tyler Moore Show*?

**A:** Yes, he's the same character. The name Lou Grant was so well-known and the character liked by so many of Mary's viewers, they gave Lou his own show.

**Q:** Why did Kate Jackson leave *Charlie's Angels*? She was always my favorite.

**A:** Sources say Kate was asked to leave the show because she didn't get along well with her co-workers and she always wanted to change her role.

Here are the three Angels who started it all: Jackie, Kate, and Farrah.

**Q:** Some of my friends think I'm weird for liking Carol Burnett but I think she is really funny. Can you please tell me why she doesn't have her own show anymore?

**A:** Carol Burnett decided to give up her successful 11-year show because she wanted to try a variety of acting jobs, not only comedy. Since her show ended, she has acted in a few serious roles in TV movies.

**Q:** It is true that Ron Howard on *Happy Days* directs some of the shows?

**A:** Yes. Ron is not only interested in acting, but also in directing and writing TV shows.

**Q:** I watched *The Waltons* the other night for the first time in a long time. I was really shocked to see how different Grandma looked. What happened to her?

**A:** Ellen Corby suffered a stroke. After a brief absence from the series, she returned, and although her speech and movement is limited, she still enjoys working on the show.

**Q:** Can you please explain how video tape recorders work? I saw a set in the store and it looked very confusing.

**A:** Video tape recorders are simple to operate, but expensive. They work like a regular tape recorder but they record the picture as well as the sound. Hook one up to a television set and then later you can play back the show on your TV screen. Some people like them because it gives them a chance to watch their favorite shows when they want.

**Q:** I really love sports shows of all kinds, especially *Wide World of Sports*. Are these shows live or are they taped?

**A:** Both. Some of the shows are taped during a live event and shown several months later; others are shown live via satellite.

**Q:** Why is it that most sports programs are on Saturday and Sunday?

**A:** Networks plan their TV schedules for their audience. More people, especially adult sports fans, are home on weekends. Also, many ball games are played on Saturday and Sunday, and they are often broadcast live.

**Q:** I have always loved watching television and would someday like to work for a TV studio. Can you tell me what I should do? I am 13.

**A:** Many junior and senior high schools offer courses in television. They can help prepare you for college courses in the same field. Careers in television include script writing, directing, and camera work.

**Q:** Why isn't the character Radar on *M\*A\*S\*H\** anymore?

**A:** Everyone was sorry to see that the character Radar was missing from the show this season. Gary Burghoff, who played Radar, decided he'd been with the series long enough. The character wasn't growing and changing anymore. He wants to try new roles — and movies!

**Q:** *Mork & Mindy* is one of the funniest shows on television. Is it true Robin Williams makes up his lines as the show goes along?

**A:** Robin gets a script just like the other actors, but it is true he often makes up things to say (ad-libs) during filming. He's very talented and funny — and sometimes what he says is a lot funnier than the script. So, he's allowed to make changes.

**Q:** Sometimes I see the word "pilot" describing a TV-show listing. What does it mean?

**What's up? Our favorite Orkan, that's what!**

**A:** A pilot is usually the first show of a new series. Although the series may not be "bought" by a network, the pilot is often shown as a TV movie, or in place of a regular series in reruns.

**Q:** What do the network initials stand for?
**A:** ABC (American Broadcasting Company), CBS (Columbia Broadcasting System), NBC (National Broadcasting Company).

**Q:** Every time I watch *The Muppet Show* I wonder if the Muppets are controlled by strings. If they are, why can't I see the strings?

**A:** The Muppets are hand or body puppets — there are only a few strings. The lights and action distract your attention, but if you look carefully, you may see a string or two.

**Q:** Why do the songs on the television commercials always seem much louder than the program, even if the volume dial remains the same?

**A:** Commercial jingles are purposely louder to attract the viewer's attention. If you turn your volume down during a commercial, you may need to turn it back up when the program continues.

**Q:** I love to watch the commercial for cat food that shows cats dancing. Are the cats really dancing, or is it trick photography?

**A:** Many cats are trained by professional animal trainers to lift their paws at a certain time. But the cat in the cat-food commercial appears to be dancing because the film is run backwards or forwards in fast motion, a trick of photography.

**Q:** I just started watching the old *I Love Lucy* shows. Were Ricky and Lucy really married when they filmed the show?

**A:** Yes. In fact, many of the situations on the show really happened to Lucy and Ricky during their marriage.

**Q:** The old *Partridge Family* shows are really neat. What is Susan Dey doing now? I know she used to be a model.

**A:** Susan Dey, now a mother and wife, has worked in several TV movies and films.

You might remember Shirley Jones when she played Shirley Partridge on the hit TV series *The Partridge Family* (now in syndicated reruns), starring with then teen-idol David Cassidy (Shaun's brother!) and Susan Dey.

**Q:** Was the girl who plays "Angie" ever in a movie? A friend said she was in *Saturday Night Fever*, but I don't remember her.

**A:** You might not remember Donna Pescow as Annette in *Saturday Night Fever*, because she has lost some weight since the movie was filmed. She played the part of the girl who wanted to be John Travolta's girlfriend.

**Q:** Is Robin Williams going to star in a movie? He is so talented, he should do something besides act on TV.

**A:** Robin will star in *Popeye*, a movie about the cartoon character who loves spinach.

**Q:** I used to love watching Cher on TV and enjoyed seeing all her different outfits. Is she performing anywhere? What has she been doing since her show on TV?

**A:** Besides opening a roller rink, Cher has appeared in nightclubs in Las Vegas.

**Q:** Does Henry Winkler ever do any movies or anything besides *Happy Days*?

**A:** Henry Winkler appeared on *Sesame Street* as The Fonz, to teach kids how to spell, brush their teeth, and tell the difference between right and wrong. He starred in two feature films, and will be playing the role of Scrooge in a new version of *A Christmas Carol*.

**Q:** There is a young woman on the old series *The Rookies* who looks a lot like Kate Jackson. Is it she?

**A:** Yes. Kate played the part of Jill before starring on *Charlie's Angels*.

# *Laverne and Shirley* . . . and Friends

*Laverne and Shirley* is one of the many television shows that is taped weekly before a live audience. And although the audience doesn't have to pay to watch, *Laverne and Shirley* is one show people probably wouldn't mind paying for. There's never an empty seat in the house. The reason is Penny Marshall (Laverne), Cindy Williams (Shirley), those Lenny and Squiggy characters, Michael McKean and David Lander — and the great warm-up before the show.

The line forms early outside the double studio doors. The crowd is in good spirits because it knows it's in for a real treat — and even a long wait in line can't upset anyone.

"Hi, thanks for coming to the show," says the studio usher with a friendly nod as he shows you to your seat. You don't have to worry about where you are going to sit, either, because the studio is set up with bleachers that enable everyone to hear everything and see all the action. Once the studio audience is seated, things begin. There is usually an announcer who welcomes everyone to the set and entertains you with stories and jokes, while the cameras are moving into position. From your bleacher seat you look down on Laverne and Shirley's apartment. You see the kitchen, the living room, and the door leading into the bed-room — and the front door. To the left is the set for Laverne's father's pizza shop. And on the right are other sets, like the brewery where the girls work and Lenny and Squiggy's living room.

Now the fun really begins as the announcer introduces Garry Marshall, the producer of the show. He chats with the audience for a while, explaining how the cameras work and answering any questions. Then one by one he introduces the stars.

There's Phil Foster, who plays Mr. DeFazio. Lenny and Squiggy come out together, making jokes, going up into the bleachers to kiss the girls, and making everyone laugh! Eddie Mecca, who plays Shirley's boyfriend, Carmine, comes

Laverne's dad (played by Phil Foster) runs the pizza joint where everybody loves to hang out. Shirley's sometime boyfriend, Carmine (Eddie Mecca), performs there by singing love ballads to all the customers.

out singing an old Italian song, and then, finally, the stars, Penny and Cindy, step out and wave hello to all.

"All right, let's get to work!" says the director, and with that, the stars take their positions on the set. The taping moves along at a fast pace, but once in a while, when someone makes a mistake, the cameras stop rolling and the scene must be redone.

Usually when that happens, one of the stars, or the director, makes a joke and the audience really laughs. The producer reminds the audience that their laughter will be recorded for the laugh track and used on the air when the show is run. "Go ahead," he says. "Laugh, whistle, shout, clap — the more you show you're enjoying the show, the better!"

Time passes quickly as the characters move from set to set, saying their lines and doing the scenes, and before you know it, the show is completed. The cameras stop, the cast and crew relax, and Penny Marshall and Cindy Williams take time to sign autographs and shake hands with the audience. It's quite an exciting experience.

And when you step down from the bleachers, pass through the double doors, and head home, you feel as if you too are a part of the *Laverne and Shirley* show!

# Lauren Tewes:
## *The Love Boat* Sails On

The perky, pretty blond lines up with everybody else to get some lunch in the studio commissary. It's been a rough day, and though she wishes she had more than 45 minutes to eat and relax, she's never been one to complain. Considering she only weighs 115 pounds and stands 5'6" tall, you'd think she could eat a bit more than a salad and juice, but not Lauren Tewes, of *The Love Boat*. "If I eat a lot it's hard to go back to work." She smiles, tossing her head so that her bouncy hair swings over her face for a second.

You might also think that spending the day on a beautiful cruise ship shouldn't be work at all. But the show is really taped 15 miles from the ocean at the 20th Century-Fox Studios. Here, a huge model of the cruise boat has been built. It has a swimming pool, dance floor, restaurant (with the captain's table), and even staterooms. In fact, the only parts of the show which really involve a ship and water are the shots of the Love Boat leaving the dock, or sometimes when special happenings take place where sailing scenes are needed.

One time the entire *Love Boat* company and that week's guest "passengers," Ray Milland

**Here's the cast from that shipshape show, *The Love Boat*. From left: Ted Lange, Lauren Tewes, Bernie Kopell, and Fred Grandy.**

and Lorne Green, headed into icy Arctic waters to do a little filming. They ran into a little trouble when huge 35-foot swells and gale winds damaged electric generators on the ship, ripped loose a gangplank, and threw the two-hour special a day behind schedule!

"If things like that happened a lot, we'd never get our show filmed," says Lauren, "so I guess it's good we do most of it in a studio — it's safer, anyway!"

Lauren puts in 10-hour days on the job, playing the ship's cruise director, Julie McCoy. She admits that, "Trying to be perky and chipper all those hours sometimes takes a lot of acting." But if she thinks that's a high price to pay for stardom, she doesn't let on. She has only nice things to say about the show and her co-stars.

"I think our show is quite good," Lauren says. "It's pretty to look at, the characters are likable, and it's very relaxing for the audience. Plus we have a very good cast."

In turn, her co-stars, Bernie Kopell, Fred Grandy, Ted Lange, and ship's captain, Gavin McLeod, have only good things to say about Lauren. "She's terrific. For somebody with as little experience as she's had — she's tremendous. She's got all the right instincts and there's something very special about her," says McLeod.

One of the things Lauren especially likes

about *Love Boat* is the great lineup of guest stars she's been able to work with. "I'm glad I got to meet Will Geer before his death," she says of the actor who made everyone love him as Grandpa Walton. "He was wonderful to work with — so professional.

"The whole atmosphere on the show is familylike. I love my co-stars," Lauren says — and the look in her eyes tells you she really means it.

# *The White Shadow:*
# They're Upfront!

If *The White Shadow* seems like the kind of television series that's very true-to-life, it's because it is. Ken Howard, who stars as Coach Ken Reeves, actually created the show from his personal experience. Back in high school, he was a six-foot-six, high-scoring basketball player nicknamed "The White Shadow" because most of the other top players on the team were black.

After high school, Ken went on to play college ball. Then he discovered acting, which led him to the Yale School of Drama and a career in show business. But underneath all that acting, Ken still loved basketball, and so the idea for the series was a natural.

Although the series is about basketball, it has dealt with some serious problems, too.

Kevin Hooks, who plays Morris Thorpe, says he's very proud of his show "because it deals with a lot of things that other television shows don't want to handle. It's easy enough for someone to make a situation comedy and keep the viewers happy, but it takes something special to make a serious and controversial show like *The White Shadow* that can still be entertaining and get in a few laughs, too."

Kevin adds that whenever he's not on the set, it seems he's always bumping into one of the cast members. "One day I was at a movie, and two girls came up and asked me if I was Kevin Hooks. When I told them I was, they wanted to know all about the show, and one of the girls really wanted to meet Ken Howard. A few minutes later, who should walk down the aisle at the same show but Ken himself! I told the girl her wish just came true."

Before winning the role on *The White Shadow*, Kevin starred in *Sounder* and *A Hero Ain't Nothing But a Sandwich*. On television, he's been in *Friendly Fire*, with Carol Burnett, and *Back Stairs at the White House*.

Although he plays a high school student in his role as Thorpe, Kevin is in his 20's. He has been married for over two years and will soon be a proud father. His favorite sport, now, is golf. It

*The White Shadow* lineup:

Top row, l to r: Eric Kilpatrick, Byron Stewart, Ken Michelman, Nathan Cook.

Bottom row, l to r: Ira Angustain, Kevin Hooks, Thomas Carter, Timmy Van Patten, and, of course, Ken Howard.

used to be basketball. But, he says, after being around a basketball all week, he doesn't want to play on the courts during his free time.

Unlike Kevin, Ira Angustain, who plays the role of Gomez, claims to love playing basketball as much as acting, and *The White Shadow* gives him the perfect combination. Ira was born in Glendale, California, August 6, 1957, and is an even six feet tall, with dark hair and brown eyes. He's been in show business since the age of three, but *Shadow* is his first television series, although he has guest starred on many favorite shows. He also starred as Freddie Prinze in the TV movie based on the life of the late actor who starred in *Chico and the Man*.

Ira, who loves all spectator sports and is an excellent basketball and baseball player, also plays the trumpet; he was a member of his school's marching band. He's single and lives in Los Angeles.

Working on *The White Shadow* takes up a good deal of his time. "Still," he says with a smile, and his expressive eyes twinkle with pleasure, "I wouldn't have it any other way."

# For Scott Baio, *Happy Days* Are Here Again!

Wonderful characters, hilarious, and often meaningful, situations, lots of fun, and a talented cast help make *Happy Days* happy viewing. In fact, Tuesday night wouldn't be the same without a visit from Henry Winkler, Ron Howard, Anson Williams, Donny Most, Scott Baio, and the rest of the *Happy Days* stars.

Although Scott Baio only joined the show as Chachi (Fonzie's cousin) last year, his character has become a popular favorite. Besides playing the drums in Richie Cunningham's band, this year he's going to be singing a lot, too.

Scott just turned 18 years old. He lives with his mom and dad, sister and brother, and a dog named Priscilla in a new home in the hills near

Hollywood. It's not too far from the studio where *Happy Days* is taped, and that's good. You see, Scott's main problem is getting up in the morning. Luckily, he has his family to help. First, the alarm clock rings — but Scott always turns it off and goes back to sleep. It's his dad's turn next. He gently shakes Scott awake and tells him it's time to get going. "Okay," a still sleepy Scott yawns, but as soon as his dad leaves the room, he's off snoozing again. So, either his mom or his brother Steven takes the next crack! His brother often calls in Priscilla, whose wet tongue is sure to get Scott sitting up quickly!

**Scott Baio may hate to wake up in the morning, but he looks wide awake in this portrait.**

Once this morning ritual is completed, Scott is ready to go. He hits the shower, eats a quick breakfast, and heads to work in his Thunderbird.

The Baio family is very close and they share a lot of time together. When Scott travels around the country filming episodes of *Hollywood Teen* (he's the host of that show), his dad or brother accompanies him. They're also always visiting him on the *Happy Days* set, where they're welcomed by the entire cast.

*Happy Days* is one series that hasn't lost any of its original cast members. At one time viewers were disappointed to learn that Henry Winkler might not be back on the show after acting in some movies. But Henry (like his fans!) loves his role as Fonzie and decided he couldn't give it up. Lucky for us! This Christmas, Henry's fans will get to see him starring as Ebenezer Scrooge in a new version of Charles Dickens' *A Christmas Carol*.

Since *Happy Days* is also syndicated around the country in daily morning reruns, followers really can have *Happy Days* every day — and that makes a lot of people extremely happy!

# Mary McDonough: A Day in Her Life on Waltons' Mountain

Did you ever wonder what a day in the life of an actress on a hit television series is like? For Mary McDonough, who plays Erin Walton, it begins early and ends late. She's up by six A.M., washes and blow-drys her hair ("I'm always in a rush in the morning," she sighs), hops into her new red Honda, and makes the half-hour drive to the Burbank Studios just before the morning freeway rush begins.

She slips her car into her personal parking place near her dressing room and hurries into the makeup department, where her hair is set on hot rollers. While the hair stylist is working on her, she sips a cup of coffee and enjoys a doughnut or roll. ("It's not good for my diet, I know," she grimaces. "But it's so good in the morning and it's the only time I break my diet.")

After her makeup is applied she goes to the wardrobe department where her clothes for the day have already been selected. Mary doesn't get to pick her own outfits — she has to wear what fits in with the script. She doesn't mind, though, because it's fun wearing the clothes girls her age wore in the 1940's.

With other members of the cast who are in this scene, Mary rehearses her lines and walks through the action. Then, the lighting is set up and filming begins. Although she may not be in every scene, she still has to stick close in case the director wants her for something. In between, while waiting, she does needlepoint, reads, or talks with the other actors and crew members, or gets a head start studying her lines for the next day.

Lunch break comes next, and Mary usually has a light salad, a glass of milk, and some fresh fruit for dessert. Or, if she's particularly hungry, she'll head for the studio commissary with Judy Norton-Tayler (her best friend and co-star), and have a cheese sandwich on wholewheat bread. Her hour up, she stops for a makeup retouching, then it's back to the set until five or six P.M..

Even though Mary just recently moved into a new home of her own, she lives about a mile

**Mary McDonough works long hours on *The Waltons*, but still manages to look pretty and relaxed.**

from her family. Usually she eats dinner with them. Her family loves hearing about her day's work, and she wants to know what they've been doing as well. After cleaning up, she goes home, takes a quick bath, and then often goes out with one of the guys she dates or with a group of friends. They'll go to a movie or maybe play a little tennis.

Then it's back home to work on her lines and hit the sack. With such a full day of work, Monday through Friday, she needs her beauty sleep!

Mary's really proud of her new home! It's a Spanish style house with four bedrooms and she's been hard at work redecorating it. She's doing the house in tones of brown, beige, tan, and white.

Mary practically grew up on *The Waltons* and admits it's hard to visualize not spending half her life on Waltons' Mountain. "We all get along terrifically," she smiles. "Michael Learned is like a second mother, and we all call Ellen Corby Grandma, even when we're not filming."

When Mary isn't filming, she likes to work with children's groups. She devotes a lot of her time to charitable causes. "I think everyone has an obligation to help those less fortunate," she says. She loves children and looks forward to a day in the future when she has children of her own. Marriage and a family are a definite "Yes!" for Mary. She loves both her families, off the set and on.

# *Taxi*:
# The Meter's
# Running!

The forecast is for clear, sunny days ahead at the Sunshine Cab Company. *Taxi* is one of the most popular of the television shows to make it past the first season. The cast is delighted to be sitting behind the wheel of a hit. And it really is one big happy family on the set and off, especially on Friday nights when the cast and crew get together to celebrate another completed show.

In fact, as soon as the director shouts, "That's a wrap!" (when taping is finished), everyone races upstairs to play disco music at full blast on a portable tape machine, dance, and party for a couple of hours.

With friends, wives, and husbands of the cast

joining in, more than 50 people are often crowded into the room. Sometimes, celebrities from other shows drop in to check out the action. Favorites are Robin Williams and some of the *Happy Days* cast. Often, John Travolta, who's a good friend of *Taxi*'s only woman driver, Marilu Henner, drops in. Jeff Conaway's new bride, Rona Newton-John, is a regular at these "Thank Heavens it's Friday" affairs.

But there's more to the cast's togetherness than just the weekly work week and party. They all play softball on Sundays, and often roller skate on Monday nights. Sometimes they take in sports functions together or go to concerts. Jeff Conaway, who plays the struggling actor Bobby, says the show's producers treat everyone like their own kids.

In the midst of a fun-loving crowd, Andy Kaufman, who plays Latka, the mechanic, keeps to himself. If he's not saying a line on stage, he rarely speaks to his fellow actors. Nothing personal, it's just his way. He says, "Most of my energies go into my other projects." Besides acting, Andy is writing a novel and is constantly working on his comedy routine. It consists of many unusual characters, all portrayed by him, with many funny voices.

The person responsible for the closeness of the *Taxi* cast is the star himself, Judd Hirsch.

Everyone calls him "Papa Judd," and he's loved for his understanding, warmth, and generosity.

The cab company's pint-sized tough guy, Danny De Vito (he plays the dispatcher, Louie), says "being mean is the hardest acting I've ever done. When I was a Boy Scout I was the only one who really helped a little old lady across the street." Danny, in his role as Louie, occasionally scratches out tunes on an old violin. But he is actually an accomplished violinist.

*Taxi*'s Judd Hirsch and Danny DeVito.

Adding a pretty face as well as more talent to the list of cabbies is Marilu Henner. She says, "We rehearse in a garage in such a relaxed atmosphere, I'm not even tired when I get home."

Maybe part of the reason is that Marilu sneaks in a few catnaps during the day. "It's fascinating how the body gets so much rest in such a short time — 10 or 15 minutes a couple of times a day can really help!" she says.

Then there are those two handsome guys, Tony Danza and Jeff Conaway. Acting since the age of nine, Jeff says show business is his life's work and the only thing he ever wants to do. It was his role in the movie *Grease* which brought him to the public's attention. It also gave him a chance to meet Olivia Newton-John's sister, Rona, whom he married. Recently, he released his first pop/rock album on Columbia Records.

Tony Danza, who plays the cabby-prize-fighter, Tony Banta, left behind a real-life boxing career to act. Even though he's a success as an actor, his first love is still boxing and he hasn't given it up, either. Just last summer, while on a break from the show, he fought at Madison Square Garden and won.

Altogether the cast of *Taxi* is definitely driving a winner, and the meter of the ratings keeps climbing higher and higher.

# A Family of Eight — On and Off Camera

As you drive up to the big gates of the Burbank Studios, where so many movies and TV shows have been filmed, you can just feel the excitement in the air. Just imagine all the famous people who have driven through those very gates in chauffeur-driven limousines. It makes you feel important just to be there.

As you turn into the driveway of gate number two, you are stopped by the guard. After you give your name, the guard checks and quickly finds your pass. He gives you a slip of paper and then shows you how to get to Stage 9, where *Eight Is Enough* is being filmed. On your way, you pass other sets and notice the marked parking spaces of some of your favorite stars — and even recognize a few familiar faces.

At last, there it is — Stage 9. You can see the parking spaces for all the *Eight Is Enough* stars — Willie Aames, Dick Van Patten, Betty Buckley, Susan Richardson, and all the gang. On the side of the sound stage where the filming takes place are rows of portable dressing rooms with the stars' names on the outside. Even Adam Rich has his own private dressing room. After all, he is one of the stars of the show, and one of the most popular at that.

Once you get to the entrance, you notice a red light is on. That means they are filming inside and must have total quiet, so you wait until you see it go off. You struggle with the big, heavy, thickly padded door, closing it softly and quietly behind you. Stepping over cords and wires and dodging ladders, cameras, props, and equipment, you make your way over to the actual set.

Inside this huge room, all the indoor scenes for the Bradford house are filmed. The rooms look exactly as they do on TV, right down to the last detail. There's so much to see, you hardly know where to look first.

Of course, you want to meet all the stars of the show. You feel as if you already know them after having watched them on TV every week, and you see at once that they really are like a family. When there's a break in filming, you often see the girls (Lani O'Grady, Lauri Walters, Susan Richardson, Dianne Kay, and Con-

The *Eight Is Enough* cast all get along wonderfully. Except for Lani O'Grady, Willie Aames, and, of course, little Adam Rich, all the Bradford children are married in real life!

nie Newton) standing around talking or going into each other's dressing trailers to chat and giggle.

The guys have a good time together, too. Adam Rich is like everybody's little brother. He loves teasing his TV brothers and sisters, and gets teased in return. And Dick Van Patten is like the Daddy to the whole clan. Just being on the set, you can feel the warmth and closeness that's shared by the entire cast. The cameramen, script supervisors, and grips (the guys who handle props and equipment) are also very much a part of the family.

"I feel very close to the people on the show," remarks Connie, who plays Elizabeth, the youngest of the girls. "We all do, and I think that's what helps the show come across so well. We're very much a family."

"When you're working on a show where you're trying to be a family, you put out an extra effort to get to know each other and really feel love. Almost two years ago our mother on the show, Diana Hyland, died — for real. That was a tremendous loss to us all, but it became a bond between us, and now we're even closer," said Susan Richardson, who plays Susan on the show.

Diane, Susan, Connie, and Grant Goodeve are all happily married now, but the gang still finds time to get together outside the show. Sometimes they have dinner at each other's homes, or play softball on the weekends. Laurie Walters says, "Dick Van Patten is the star, but he never acts like a star. He's genuine on and off the set. That's unusual in Hollywood.

"I think one reason the show is so successful," Laurie says, "is because it reassures America that family life is good and it's possible. Off camera, too, all of us believe it. My best friends in Hollywood are the Bradford kids."

# The *240 Robert* Gang

If you're looking for adventure, excitement, and good acting, then you probably watch *240 Robert* each week. With a cast like John Perry, Joanna Cassidy, and Mark Harmon, the show has really got a lot going for it!

John Perry plays the role of Deputy Trap, one of the dedicated officers of the Los Angeles Sheriffs' Search and Rescue Unit. Acting is a very important part of John's life, but he also counts music high on his list. In fact, his big show-business break came when he auditioned for and became the lead singer with the Serendipity Singers.

John was born in Williamstown, Massachusetts, and says he'll always be a small-town boy at heart. He was on the football team, and president of the glee club. Then he went on to college where he spent a lot of time singing with the choir and performing in drama presentations.

A tall and slender guy, John stands six-feet, two-inches tall and has brown hair and blue eyes. He feels working on *240 Robert* is wonderful — he enjoys his work and gets along well with his co-stars.

In his role as Deputy Thibideaux (that's spelled correctly!) Mark Harmon works side by side with Deputy Trap and Deputy Morgan (Joanna Cassidy). He plays a bright, eager, and dedicated young man who spends his days saving lives.

Mark comes from a show-business family. His mom, Elyse Knox, was an actress, and his dad, Tom Harmon, is a former football pro turned sports announcer and radio personality. What's more, Mark's sister, Kris, married Rick Nelson — one of the teen idols of the 1950's, and Mark made his acting debut on Rick's dad's TV series, *Ozzie's Girls*.

You probably don't remember Mark's other series, *Sam*, since it was cancelled before it even got started, but it was about a young policeman and his dog, Sam. Mark later won an Emmy for his performance in *Franklin and*

**John Perry, Joanna Cassidy, and Mark Harman star as the dedicated officers of the Los Angeles Sheriffs' Search and Rescue Unit in ABC-TV's tension-filled drama series *240 Robert*.**

*Eleanor: The White House Years*, and although working on *240 Robert* keeps him busy, he still managed to star in the movie *Beyond the Poseidon Adventure*, with Sally Field and Michael Caine.

When he's not working, Mark enjoys browsing through antique shops, looking for items to decorate his apartment. He lives in the Hollywood Hills (he's a bachelor!) and is a strict vegetarian. He likes cooking with a Chinese wok and playing with his pets, a dog named Ryan and a cat called Arnold.

Mark is definitely a handsome guy, and he is six feet tall with dark-blond hair and sparkling blue eyes. His friends all say he's got a great sense of humor and is a great guy to know. We agree!

# *Out of the Blue — to You!*

Take a family of orphaned children and a guardian angel watching over them, and what have you got? ABC-TV's comedy series, *Out of the Blue*. Take Jimmy Brogan, Clark Brandon, Tami Lauren, Shane and Jason Keller, and Hanna Dean, and what else have you got? A terrific cast!

Jimmy Brogan, who plays the angel sent to Earth to help guide this recently orphaned family, was born in Boston, but his family moved to Chicago and then to Ohio, where Jimmy was graduated from St. Ignatius High School back in 1966. Although Jimmy always had a secret desire to perform as a comedian, he never really thought of acting as a career, and when he enrolled at the University of Notre Dame he majored in sociology. After completing those studies, he stayed on to do graduate work in business administration and educational counseling, and in 1972 he went to New York to work in politics. A far cry from a show-business career, right? It was in New York that Jimmy decided to test his comic talents, and he began performing at little clubs; he then moved to bigger ones, such as Catch A Rising Star, Improvisation, and Folk City. Finally he was discovered by Woody Allen's managers and he was on his way.

Born on September 18th, six-feet, two-inch Jimmy has dark-brown hair and blue eyes, and absolutely loves playing an angel — but then he is an angel of a guy.


You probably remember Clark Brandon from his previous roles on television — he starred in the series *The Fitzpatricks* and on *The Big Blue Marble*, and he's guest starred on top shows like *Wonder Woman* and *Fantasy Island*.

In his role as Chris on *Out of the Blue*, Clark is the head of the family, even though he plays a teenager on the show.

Born in New York on December 30, 1958, Clark is five-feet, ten-inches tall. He keeps in shape by horseback riding, skiing, swimming, and playing tennis — even though working on his new series doesn't give him much free time anymore. He's usually up in the morning by six A.M., at work by seven, and not home until seven P.M.

Of course, at work he gets an hour or two off for lunch, but with his popularity, even his lunch hours have been spent doing interviews or photo sessions. Still, Clark's not one to complain. He likes nothing more than doing what he loves best, and that's acting.

In fact, Clark says he gets very restless when he's not working. "If I have more than a week off at one time, I go bananas," he smiles. "Work is like therapy to me — it's soothing." And that's lucky for his thousands of fans who write to him at ABC-TV weekly, asking for autographs, pictures, information, or just writing to say "hello."

And Clark loves getting fan mail, too. Although he doesn't have time to read and answer it all, he can be found reading his fan mail on the set in between filming.

Clark is very close to his mom and dad, Peter and Jane Brandon, and his sister, Mary, and until last summer he lived at home with them. Now he has an apartment in Santa Monica, but it's not far from his folks, so he can still drop by to visit them when he has some time.

Clark says one of the most embarrassing things that ever happened to him was while working on *The Fitzpatricks*. "We had finished shooting a scene for the day," Clark tells the story, "and the director said, 'That's a wrap — see you later, Clark,' and I thought he meant we were through filming for the day. So, since I wanted to go and price some tires for my car, I left and didn't come back until the next day. When I got there, the director was upset and asked where I had gone. When I told him what had happened, he realized it was an honest mistake, but I guess I ruined the entire afternoon's shooting. I was supposed to be in the next scene, and since I wasn't there, they couldn't film. Oh well, the crew loved me — they got to go home early!"

Clark Brandon loves reading fan mail, so he should have a great year while starring in *Out of the Blue*.

Clark's the kind of guy who is a country boy at heart. He loves the wide open spaces, walking in the rain, and, yes, even though he lives in southern California, he enjoys cold mornings when you can bundle up in a coat and hat and fight the wind when you walk. He also likes the color orange, chocolate eclairs, and admits his biggest weakness is for pizza. "I love it. I could eat it three times a day — *any* way. I love everything on it, or just cheese and tomatoes. I can't say no to a pizza!"

# The TV Whiz Quiz

Do you think you know a lot about TV? Take the *TV Whiz Quiz* and find out just how much you really do know. Some of the questions are true or false, some are fill-ins, and some are multiple choice. Ready? Go! The answers are at the end, but don't peek!

1) Tony Banta is a character from which of the following TV series: a. *Happy Days* b. *Dallas* c. *The Dukes of Hazzard* d. *Taxi*

2) True or False: Shelley Hack, a cosmetics model, replaced Kate Jackson on *Charlie's Angels*.

It looks like it's bad news — again — for Jack in *Three's Company*.

3) True or False: Melissa Sue Anderson played the role of Dana in the TV movie *Survival of Dana*.

4) How did Mork arrive on planet Earth? a. on a jumbo jet  b. in an egg  c. on a falling star  d. in a spaceship

5) True or False:  Scott Baio plays the part of Squiggy on *Laverne and Shirley*.

6) True or False:  Ken Howard from *The White Shadow* series is related to Ron Howard from *Happy Days*.

Jimmy McNichol gets a whale of a kiss from Shamu, Sea World's three-ton killer whale star. Jimmy loves amusement parks — especially those with roller coasters — and whales!

7) Farrah Fawcett-Majors was born in: a. Corpus Christi, Texas  b. Tampa, Florida  c. Dallas, Texas  d. New York City.

8) What television series is Loni Anderson on?

_____

9) Ricardo _____ and Herve _____ are the stars of *Fantasy Island*. What are the names of the characters they portray?
_____ and _____

10) True or False: Bob Hope appeared on Leif Garrett's first television special.

11) Who are the two actresses who played the part of Nancy Drew on *The Hardy Boys?* _____ and _____.

12) On *The Partridge Family*, the part of Laurie Partridge was played by: a. Marlo Thomas b. Tatum O'Neal c. Susan Dey d. Quinn Cummings

13) Mork's mission on Earth is to: a. fall in love with Mindy b. observe and report c. help Earthlings discover their emotions d. fill the Earth with Orkans

14) On *Three's Company*, the role of _____ is played by Joyce DeWitt.

**Larry Wilcox is something of a cowboy, and took to roping sheep during a break on location for *CHiPs*.**

15) On *I Love Lucy*, Lucy and Ricky's good friends are:   a. Beth and Bill   b. Jane and Frank   c. Ethel and Fred   d. Sally and Tom

16) True or False:   Beautiful Susan Anton had a four-week special show called *Starring Susan Anton*.

17) *All in the Family* did not return this fall, but the series co-star, Carroll O'Connor, returned with a new show called:   a. *Archie's Bar and Grill*   b. *Bunker's Bar*   c. *Archie Bunker's Place*   d. *Archie's*

18) True or False:   The Ropers were the landlords of the apartment building on *The Jeffersons*.

19) On *Quincy*, Jack Klugman plays the part of:   a. a detective   b. a medical examiner   c. a lawyer   d. a reporter

20) In the series *Roots*, the part of young Kunta Kinte was played by _____.

21) The name of the cute space mongrel on *Battlestar Galactica* was _____.

22) True or False:   Lauren Tewes plays the part of the ship's cruise director on *The Love Boat*.

23) Bottling beer is the occupation of:   a. Fonzie   b. Lenny and Squiggy   c. Laverne and Shirley   d. Barney Miller

24) True or False:   On *Charlie's Angels*, Charlie has never been seen.

114

25) The character that John Travolta played on *Welcome Back, Kotter* was _____.

26) True or False: Michael Ontkean once played Willie Gillis on *The Rookies*.

27) True or False: Jimmy McNichol played the part of a football player in the TV movie *Champions*.

There are many similarities between Tony Danza and his *Taxi* character, Tony Banta. They both love boxing, are soft-spoken, and adore children!

28) Marie Osmond made her dramatic TV debut in: a. *The Initiation of Sarah* b. *A Gift of Love* c. *Women at West Point* d. *A Very Special Love*

29) On *The Hardy Boys*, Frank Hardy was played by _____.

30) True or False: The action on *Alice* takes place in a small-town pizza parlor.

31) When Rob Reiner and Sally Struthers left *All in the Family*, the characters they played, Mike and Gloria,: a. moved to California b. got a divorce c. disappeared after a fight with Archie d. vacationed in Europe

32) Officer Jon Baker is a character on _____ and is played by _____.

Here are Lance Kerwin and Scott Baio in a scene from a TV movie.

33) Guests come to *Fantasy Island* so they can: a. fall in love b. get away from day-to-day routine c. live out the fantasy of their heart's desire d. none of these

34) True or False: Peter Barton was a model before he starred on the television show *Shirley*.

35) Christopher Reeve played Superman in the movie. What was the name of the actor who played him on the old television series? a. Jim Connors b. Robert Wagner c. George Reeves d. Jimmy Olsen

36) True or False: In the 1950's, *American Bandstand* was broadcast live from Philadelphia.

37) Denis Cole (Jaclyn Smith's husband) used to play on the TV series: a. *The Mod Squad* b. *Marcus Welby, M.D.* c. *That Girl* d. None of these.

38) The name of the soda shop on *Happy Days* is: a. Big Al's b. Arnold's c. The Hum Dinger d. Fonzarelli's

39) True or False: Robert Urich is Dan Tana on *Vegas*.

40) On *The Bionic Woman*, Jamie Sommers' strength was in her: a. right eye b. little finger c. big toe d. left leg

41) On *Taxi*, Jeff Conaway plays the role of Bobby, who is: a. a taxi driver by day and law student at night b. an aspiring ac-

tor   c. an aspiring prize fighter   d. an aspiring rock singer.

42) True or False:   Tom Wopat plays the part of Bo Duke on *The Dukes of Hazzard*.

43) True or False:   Erik Estrada always has a stand-in when he's filmed riding his motorcycle on *CHiPs*.

Here are the guys from *The Dukes of Hazzard*.

44) What are the names of the Bradford children on *Eight Is Enough?*

_____,
_____,
_____,
_____,
_____,
_____,
_____,
_____.

45) *Like Normal People* was a TV movie: a. starring Leif Garrett  b. directed by Tony Danza  c. turned down by John Travolta  d. starring Shaun Cassidy

46) Bill Bixby's character turns into The Hulk when:  a. the moon is full  b. David Banner becomes fearful of the situation  c. stress begins to mount  d. he becomes nervous

47) The Fonz lives:  a. with his parents  b. in an apartment over the Cunninghams' garage  c. with Potsy  d. with his Aunt Jane

48) True or False:  Quinn Cummings plays the role of Buddy on *Family*.

49) On *Diff'rent Strokes*, how did Arnold and Willis become part of the Drummond household?  a. Mr. Drummond adopted them from an orphanage  b. they showed up on his doorstep and he couldn't part with

them  c. he took the kids when their mother deserted them  d. when his housekeeper died, she asked her boss to please take care of her children

50) True or False:  Boss Hogg is the name of a town in *The Dukes of Hazzard*.

With his huge talent, who knows how far Gary Coleman will go!

# Answers to The TV Whiz Quiz

1) d
2) True
3) True
4) b
5) False
6) False
7) a
8) *WKRP in Cincinnati*
9) Montalban, Villechaize:
   Roarke, Tatoo
10) True
11) Pamela Sue Martin,
    Janet Johnson
12) c
13) b
14) Janet
15) c
16) True
17) c
18) False
19) b
20) Lavar Burton
21) Muffet
22) True
23) c
24) True
25) Barbarino
26) True

27) False
28) b
29) Parker Stevenson
30) False
31) a
32) *CHiPs*,
Larry Wilcox
33) c
34) True
35) c
36) True
37) d
38) b
39) True
40) d
41) b
42) False
43) False
44) Susan, Nancy, David,
Elizabeth, Joannie, Mary,
Nicholas, Tommy
45) d
46) b,c,d
47) b
48) False
49) d
50) False